A Small Family Murder

A Play

Simon Brett

A SAMUEL FRENCH ACTING EDITION

SAMUEL
FRENCH

FOUNDED 1830

SAMUELFRENCH-LONDON.CO.UK
SAMUELFRENCH.COM

FOR AMATEUR PRODUCTION ENQUIRIES

UNITED KINGDOM AND WORLD EXCLUDING NORTH AMERICA
plays@SamuelFrench-London.co.uk
020 7255 4302/01

Each title is subject to availability from Samuel French,

depending upon country of performance.

A SMALL FAMILY MURDER

First performed at the Arundel Football Club as part
of the Arundel Festival Drip Action Theatre Trail,
devised by Bill Brennan.

All of the characters were played by Simon Brett

Directed by Simon Brett

CHARACTERS

Craig Maudsley, Detective Inspector
Gavin Trevelyan, late 40s
Miles Trevelyan, Gavin's brother, early 50s
Lionel Trevelyan, their father

SYNOPSIS OF SCENES

The action of the play takes place in an anonymous small space that could represent a police interview room or a small meeting room in an old people's home.

Time — the present

AUTHOR'S NOTE

A Small Family Murder features five characters, two of whom do not appear on stage. Detective Inspector Craig Maudsley is heard in voice-over, but Detective Constable Alice Parker is unheard as well as unseen. The two detectives are imagined to be in the two chairs facing away from the audience, and the three interviewees address their statements to them, apparently reacting to the detectives' (unheard) questions.

The play can be produced with four actors playing the four speaking parts, though I think it gains from having all the characters played by the same actor. (There are lines about "family likeness" which are strengthened by the doubling.) Having done it myself, I know that *A Small Family Murder* is a tough learn, but in performance a very rewarding experience. Have fun with it.

S.B.

A SMALL FAMILY MURDER

SCENE 1

The setting throughout is an anonymous small space that could represent a police interview room or a small meeting room in an old people's home. There is a table with one institutional chair behind it and two institutional chairs in front, facing away from the audience. It is twelve-fourteen p.m. on a Thursday

During the following announcement Gavin Trevelyan enters and takes a seat. He is a well-educated man in his late forties, who believes, erroneously, that he can get through life on charm alone

Maudsley (*voice-over*) Investigation into the death of Mrs Valerie Trevelyan. Interview conducted in Interview Room Two of the Fedborough Major Crime Unit with the dead woman's younger son, Mr Gavin Trevelyan. Present at the interview are Detective Inspector Craig Maudsley and Detective Constable Alice Parker. Interview begun and recording started at twelve-fourteen p.m. on Thursday the sixteenth of August.

Gavin Obviously I'm devastated by my mother's death. I'm still really in shock, and I think it's going to take me a long time to come to terms with what's happened. Yes, I am Gavin Trevelyan, and I was the one who found her body.

I suppose, looking for positives in this unhappy situation, she is at least no longer in pain. She had been ill and she hated being in that nursing home. Hated having sacrificed her independence. So this is, I suppose — funny how the clichés come up at a time like this — a merciful release.

(Reacting to a question) What was my relationship with my mother? I'm sorry, I'm not used to being questioned by such a stunningly attractive woman ... Alice, was it? *(He chuckles. There is a pause)* Very well, Detective Constable Parker. Well, me and my mother were, you know, like mothers and sons are. I adored her, and I like to think the feeling was mutual. That's why I'm so devastated.

Very well, the last time I saw her — before I actually found her dead — it was earlier the same evening. Yes, my father and my brother Miles did also visit her that evening. A coincidence, maybe, but in the event a happy coincidence. It was as if we all had a chance to pay our last respects.

How was she looking? Frail, I would say, very frail. All swathed up in bedclothes. I could only see her face ... so terribly thin. The doctor who looked after her at the nursing home had apparently said it could happen any time. I'm just glad that I managed to see her so near the end. *(He pauses)* Yes, all right, I admit I hadn't seen my mother that much over recent years. I've been living abroad. And the reason I came back was that I'd had a message from my elder brother Miles, saying that he reckoned the old girl was on the way out. So I thought I should come and, thank heaven, I just made it in time to ... As I say, I'm devastated.

Do I know what killed my mother? Well, I assume cancer. Cancer of the stomach. That's what she was suffering from. Painful, sad, but we've all got to die of something.

Poisoned? No, I don't believe it. Good heavens, Inspector, surely not? An overdose of her own painkillers? That's terrible. That place is meant to have trained nursing staff, they shouldn't make a mistake like that. Mind you, the nurse who showed me to my mother's room was ... Well, let's just say I don't think English was her first language, know what I mean?

Not an accident? Inspector, do I understand you correctly? You're saying my mother was murdered? But why would anyone want to murder her?

Her will? Well, I assume she had made one, though I've no idea what its provisions might be. No, I didn't know that she had made a new will recently. (*He pauses*) Though had I thought about it, there would have been a kind of logic — I mean, given the state my father was in.

Yes, his degeneration happened while I was living abroad. When I left, which is — what, five years ago? — he still very much had all his marbles. Was still the senior partner in Trevelyan's. One of the sharpest solicitors around. People used to say, "If you've got a legal problem, then Lionel Trevelyan's your man." Mr Fix-It. They said he could have got a driving licence for Stevie Wonder. But then he started to get forgetful, started making errors at work and, you know, the brain was gone. I have this information from my mother. She always kept in touch with me, wherever I was. As I said, we were very close.

No, I can't pretend that I was close to my brother Miles. As children we had very little in common. There is said to be a family likeness between us, though I can't see it myself. Anyway, we have very different personalities. Miles always had a rather sneaky, calculating streak, whereas I was ... more of a free spirit. No surprise that he became a solicitor. One of my former girlfriends said that I got the family charm, and Miles ... didn't.

Joint beneficiaries of our mother's will? Are we? I didn't know that. Look, the only contact I had back here was with my mother, and she didn't mention it.

Why did I go back to see her a second time on the evening she died? Yes, it must seem odd to you, Inspector, and in a way I don't have a very logical explanation for my behaviour. Have you ever had a premonition, Constable? A bad feeling, a feeling that something unpleasant is about to happen? (*He pauses*) Ah. Well, I have had that kind of sensation, rather often. A woman I once knew — well, let's be honest, one of my lovers — said that I was psychic, that I had the ability to anticipate the future. And it's true. I do get an instinct for things that are about to happen. Particularly bad things.

And that's what I felt that evening with my mother. I'd been to see her, left about six-thirty. I went then, because I knew my father was due there about seven, and I didn't want to see him. No, no lack of love. When he was in his prime, we got on very well. But the thought of seeing him in his current state ... I'm sorry, I chickened out.

I don't know why the staff at his place kept taking him to see my mother. I suppose she insisted. From all accounts, the two of them couldn't have had much in the way of communication. Apparently my father doesn't even know who he is, let alone anyone else. But I suppose my mother must have got some comfort out of his visits.

Yes, very well. I'll tell you exactly what happened on my second visit to her room that evening. Not much to tell, really. As I say, I had this premonition that something was wrong, so I went back to the nursing home. Sorry? Probably just after eight. Anyway, I was told at reception that my brother Miles was with her. I didn't want to muscle in on his visit and, quite honestly, I didn't particularly want to see him, so I went to the local pub for half an hour. Yes, *The Red Cow*. People will have seen me there. You can check it if you want to. When I got back to the nursing home — maybe a quarter to nine that would be — they told me that Miles had left some time before. He must have gone just after I went to the pub. So I went upstairs to my mother's room. The premonition within me was now very strong. When I pushed open the door, there was very little light. I could just see the outline of her propped up on the bed, but I knew there was something wrong. I listened hard, but could hear no sound of breathing. I went and very gently touched her shoulder. There was no reaction. I put on the lights, and a quick look confirmed what I had feared. I immediately rang down to the nursing home's reception and told them what had happened.

Anything different from the earlier time I'd seen her? Not much that I — oh, one thing. She'd wrapped a scarf around her neck. I think she felt the cold terribly, even though it's midsummer. And people are supposed to feel cold as death approaches, aren't they?

Yes, Inspector, I have heard that old chestnut about the person who finds the body being the first suspect. So if I have cast myself in that role ... maybe you'll be good enough to tell me how I am supposed to have murdered the old girl? I'm sorry, but you have more information on that subject than I do. So tell me — how did I do it? I know I used painkillers, but how did I get my mother to swallow them in sufficient quantities to —— Oh, I forced her mouth open, did I? And forced down a liquid solution of the painkillers that I had prepared earlier and diluted with an orange drink? How very clever of me.

Well, if that's what I did, I'm sure you won't have any difficulty in proving it. Come on, I may not be a professional policeman, but I have heard of DNA. Surely, if I did to my mother what you're suggesting I did to her, there'd be my DNA all over the place. On her body, on the cup she drank from ... Wouldn't there?

Oh, I wore gloves. How thoughtful of me. Traces of leather around her neck. Then surely you can test the gloves for ... (*He pauses*) The gloves have disappeared.

So what have you got against me, Inspector Maudsley? Just a few suppositions, I would say. Opportunity? Yes, I suppose I had that, assuming I would want to kill a woman whom ... (*His voice begins to break*) I have adored throughout my entire life. And motive? Oh yes, the new will. The new will of whose provisions I was — until you just told me about them — completely ignorant.

I don't really see, Inspector, that you have any reason to detain me longer. If you continue to insist that my mother's death was murder, then I suggest you leave me alone and go out to find the real perpetrator. And now, if you'll excuse me ...

He makes to leave, but something the inspector says stops him

What do you mean — you've found things out about my background? I left England for business reasons. Yes, all right, I was bankrupt. (*He slumps back into his chair*) And debts. There were debts. I'd had a lot of bad luck. Going abroad was going to wipe the slate clean. I needed something steady. That's why I went in for selling apartments in Northern Cyprus. "A licence to print money" — that's how my partner Ahmet described it. But we had a bit of bad luck there too. No, I wasn't aware this country had no extradition treaty with Northern Cyprus.

Look, all right, if you insist — I'm skint. And I do have a lot of debts, yes. And when I heard about — I mean, had I heard about my mother's new will earlier ... Well, I suppose some people might have seen it as an opportunity. But I didn't. My mind doesn't work like that. I mean, even assuming that I did know about the will — which, as I've told you, I didn't — I wouldn't be capable of raising my hand against my own mother. Are you sure this isn't a mistake? Are you sure she really was murdered? (*He pauses*) Well, if you are, you must still see that it's ridiculous to suspect me.

My brother Miles, on the other hand ... He stands to benefit from the new will just as much as I do. And, knowing him, I bet he actually drafted it. Come on, Miles is a solicitor. He's now senior partner of Trevelyan's. Yes, this whole thing has his pawprints all over it. I bet it was Miles who persuaded my parents to change the will. Transferring all Dad's assets to Mum, that's how his mind works too. And it would be absolutely typical of him to have set this whole thing up and — Just a minute ... At the moment, if everything runs smoothly, he'll only get fifty per cent of the loot. Miles won't like that. He wants it all. He's already taken over Mum and Dad's big house and moved them out into a little flat. He's taken over Dad's position at Trevelyan's. He's ...

Oh, my God, what's he said about me? Have you talked to him yet about the case? (*He pauses*) Only a little? What's "a little"? I bet, if I know anything about my brother, that "little" included a few details which got you suspicious of me. Yes, that'd make sense. Our mother's found murdered and who's the obvious suspect? The prodigal brother, the one who's had bad luck, the one who's got money problems, the one who found the body.

Well, my advice to you, Detective Inspector Maudsley and Detective Constable Parker, would be to have a much more detailed chat with my brother. Don't forget, he was the last person with my mother before I found her. I think you'll get a lot more interesting information out of Miles Trevelyan than you ever will out of me. (*He rises to his feet*) And now, since I'm only talking to you out of goodwill — and you have no powers to keep me here longer than is necessary — I would like to tell you that my limited stock of goodwill has run out, and I am leaving. Goodbye!

Gavin storms off

The Lights fade to Black-out

SCENE 2

The same, about an hour later. During the following announcement Miles Trevelyan enters. He is a buttoned-up solicitor with rimless glasses, in his early fifties

Maudsley (*voice-over*) Investigation into the death of Mrs Valerie Trevelyan. Interview conducted in Interview Room Two of the Fedborough Major Crime Unit with the dead woman's older son, Mr Miles Trevelyan. Present at the interview are Detective Inspector Craig Maudsley and Detective Constable Alice Parker. Interview begun and recording started at one twenty-seven p.m. on Thursday the sixteenth of August.

Miles Is this going to take long? Because I do have a busy practice to run, you know. Very well, Inspector. (*He sits in the chair*) You don't need to tell me about the demands of the law. It is a world in which I have spent my entire professional life. So, if we could get our business concluded as quickly as possible ...

Yes, I am senior partner of Trevelyan's solicitors' practice in Fedborough. I have had that role since my father's retirement, due to ill health, some four and a half years ago. I'm afraid, from having a fine mind and an acute legal brain, his memory started to fail him and ... age is cruel.

Yes, I have an enduring power of attorney to look after my father's affairs. Once he started to deteriorate, that seemed the most logical course to take. I did not want my mother troubled by such responsibilities.

Yes, and I did arrange the sale of the big house in which they had brought up myself and my brother Gavin. With my father in a care home, the place was too big for my mother. I organized the purchase of a small flat for her, convenient for the shops and near to her friends. And that's where she stayed until her illness necessitated her removal to a nursing home where she could have twenty-four hour care.

Yes, I did buy the family house myself for my wife and children. Constable Parker, I resent that insinuation. I paid the going market rate for the property. The only saving that was made was by not involving an estate agent. Which seemed pointless as the transaction was within the family. But I can assure you that all the paperwork for the purchase is in order.

No, Inspector, of course Trevelyan's did not handle the conveyancing on the deal. That would have been most inappropriate. I would never let my company work on any legal matter from which I might prove to be a beneficiary. The work was done by another firm, Skilling and Bates. (*He pauses*) I agree, Mr Skilling is a good friend of mine, but I can assure you I know the boundaries between my friendships and my professional life.

My mother's will? Yes, I thought you would probably want to talk about that. I should say straight away that the new will was drawn up with my mother's full agreement. Given the state that my father was in, it was the logical thing to do. He was no longer capable of making decisions for himself, and I didn't want my mother to be left with the aggravation of dealing with his estate after his death. So an agreement was drawn up, whereby all the assets of Lionel Trevelyan were made over to Valerie Trevelyan, and a trust fund was set up to pay for my father's nursing home care for the duration of his life. And before you ask, no, none of the legal work on the will was done by Trevelyan's either. (*He pauses*) Yes, Skilling and Bates again, as it happens.

What? Yes, my mother's death will mean that my father gets nothing from her estate. And my brother Gavin and I are the beneficiaries of her will, yes. In the emotion of the moment I hadn't really considered that ramification.

Gavin? I hear that you have spoken to him, Sergeant Parker. Yes, there is said to be a family likeness between us, though I can't see it myself. Anyway, we have very different personalities.

My relationship with Gavin? Hmm, well, there's no point in beating about the bush. It has to be said we never had a great deal in common. Gavin was one of those people who thought he could get through life on charm alone — something which I have never aspired to do. I've always believed in the value of hard work. I've no idea why he came back to England when he did. Maybe he'd run up too many debts in Northern Cyprus. That would have been in character.

What? No, I certainly didn't suggest he should come back here. I've had no contact with Gavin since he went abroad to escape his creditors. He has never been good with money and always sailed very close to the wind. No, I have no proof that he ever did anything illegal, but were I to hear that he had, well, let's say it wouldn't surprise me.

I would imagine that Gavin came back to England because he'd heard about the changes to our father's will. How might he have heard that? Certainly not from me, no. I would think the most likely thing to have happened is that our mother wrote to him and told him. She always had an unaccountably soft spot for Gavin. His glib, surface charm worked for her.

Very well, the evening of my mother's death. (*He pauses*) Since she went into the nursing home, I had been in the habit of visiting her on a Wednesday evening, at eight o'clock. We had little to talk about, but I thought it was my duty to keep going. I never stayed longer than half an hour — I didn't wish to tire her. That evening she was quieter than usual. She looked very frail. And I think, even though it was high summer, she must have been feeling the cold. Certainly she had blankets piled up over her, and a scarf wrapped around her throat.

As I say, she looked very frail. When I heard, later that evening, that she had passed away, it came as no surprise. A merciful release, I would have said. As soon as I heard from my mother's doctor what had happened, I went straight to the care home where my father lives. The news was not of the kind that could be relayed by a third party — it had to be delivered face to face. So I told him that my mother had passed away, though whether he took it in I have no means of knowing.

I can assure you, Constable, that when I left my mother that evening she was ... to say in perfect health would not be appropriate, but she was no worse than when I arrived. Very definitely still alive.

I'm afraid, Inspector, that I'm still having difficulty in believing your claim that my mother was murdered by an overdose of painkillers. (*World-wearily*) I agree, Inspector, it's possible that a regular visitor to my mother could have stolen the painkillers from her on a regular basis. But I can't imagine who would do such a thing. And I can assure you that I wouldn't!

A more likely scenario, I would imagine, is that that my mother herself had been hoarding the painkillers with a view to ending her own life, and putting a stop to the increasing pain that she was suffering. And that is what she did.

No, Constable, I admit that doesn't explain the bruising about the neck and jaw. But old people have falls, they bump into things. They bruise easily.

Traces of leather around the bruises? If you say so. (*Deeply offended*) Yes, Inspector, I do possess a pair of leather gloves, but I haven't seen them for months. Do I have to remind you that we are in the middle of a rather hot August?

(*Looking at the detectives; bewildered*) Am I seriously to believe that you think I might have killed my mother? Well, that's preposterous — and quite possibly actionable.

What? A more pertinent question might be who else saw my mother that evening. Well, in a murder case you can't rule out the nursing home staff, if you believe what you read in the Sunday papers. My father you probably can rule out. I don't think he now has the intellectual capacity to plan a crime as complex as this one seems to be. (*He pauses*) And then of course there is Gavin. He is co-beneficiary of the will, so if you were reckoning I had a financial motive for murder, exactly the same applies to him. And his need would undoubtedly be greater than mine. Debt follows Gavin around like a shadow.

Do I think he's capable of committing a murder? (*There is a long pause*) Look, I have no wish to speak ill of my brother, but there is something of which I think you should be aware — given the nature of the investigation that you are currently involved in. The fact is that Gavin's — what I fear must be called his "romantic life" — has not always run smoothly. He is, not to put too fine a point on it, something of a womanizer. Nothing wrong in that, you may say. But it is also a fact that in some of his relationships, violence figured. More than one of his girlfriends complained that Gavin hit them — and there was one who actually threatened to take him to court.

Fortunately, the situation was resolved, which is why you won't find any official record of it. Our father managed to persuade the girl against litigation. I think some financial arrangement may have been agreed — it wouldn't have been the first time our father had bailed Gavin out — and everything was hushed up. Now I hope my telling you this isn't going to prejudice you against my brother, but I did think it was my duty to let you know about it.

(*Looking at his watch*) And now, if you don't have any further questions to ask, I do have a practice to run. (*He stands*) Don't hesitate to contact me if there is any other information you require. But I must get back to the office. The business of the law must continue to be done. Good afternoon.

He exits

The Lights fade to Black-out

The same, later that afternoon. During the following announcement Lionel Trevelyan enters and takes the seat. He is very old and bent and walks with a stick. As he moves, he hums a tuneless little tune to himself

Maudsley (*voice-over*) Investigation into the death of Mrs Valerie Trevelyan. Interview with the dead woman's husband, Mr Lionel Trevelyan. Because of the frailty of the witness, this interview is being conducted at the Yew Tree Retirement Home in Fedborough. Present at the interview are Detective Inspector Craig Maudsley and Detective Constable Alice Parker. Interview begun and recording started at three forty-eight p.m. on Thursday the sixteenth of August.

Lionel Very good of you to come all this way to see me. Not the most salubrious of environments — always smells of pee — but I suppose you can't have everything. And I dare say I contribute to the smell of pee as much as anyone else, so … Probably more, actually. (*He chuckles and wheezes*)

Now remind me who you are. I'm sorry, I get mixed up. Have you come about mending the television aerial? Or is it to cut my hair? Or my toe-nails? I know somebody comes to do that. If it's the television aerial, I ask you to be gentle. Very gentle. The side of my head where they fixed up the last one still hurts. And the reception on Channel Five is dreadful. Mind you, so are the programmes, so it's no great loss.

He hums the tuneless little tune and looks to the back of the room

Oh, I see Rosa Klebb's here. She's one of my nurses. Say hallo, Rosa. Say hallo to the nice television aerial people. You don't need to stay, Rosa. I'm sure you've got other patients to bully.

Lionel watches Rosa exit

Bye-bye. (*After a pause*) She's not really called Rosa Klebb, you know. My name for her, that's all. It just fits her personality.

Valerie? Oh, you're here to talk about Valerie. Valerie's death, you say? Valerie's dead? Funny, she didn't tell me. You'd have thought she'd have had the decency to tell me, wouldn't you? It's the kind of thing that could affect our plans quite considerably.

(*Suddenly lucid*) See her? Yes, I remember seeing her. Wednesday it was, Wednesday evening. I was taken to see Valerie. At the nursing home. Not at that pokey little flat that Miles forced her into.

No, of course I didn't go on my own. They don't let me go anywhere on my own. They're afraid they'll lose me. So Rosa Klebb took me to see Valerie. I don't like being in the car with Rosa Klebb. Too close. I'm afraid sharp little blades are going to come out of her toecaps and make me "deaded". (*He gives a little Goon-like chuckle*)

But Rosa Klebb didn't come to Valerie's room with me. Having got me to the place, she left me to my own devices. She stayed with the girl at reception, discussing new refinements in equipment for the torturing of geriatrics. (*He chuckles, then goes off into a reverie*)

Valerie. Valerie, I'm so sick of doing conveyancing. Shall I give up the law altogether? Shall you and I just go off and live in the sun on the Isle of Capri? No, you wouldn't want to leave the cats, would you, Valerie? Or your plumbago.

What was it you said about Valerie? Oh, dead, yes. Knew it was something.

No, she was fine when I left her on the Wednesday evening. Fine. Well, I say "fine". She was obviously very ill, but she was breathing. And at our age that's the minimum one aspires to.

What's that — an overdose of painkillers? Well, in a way that seems very apposite, because Valerie had been suffering from an overdose of

pain. Painkillers, painkillers ... Always makes me think of something
... Oh yes, the knickers girls of Valerie's generation used to wear for
school. Pain kill— No, those were "passion-killers", weren't they?
Something else they were called ... What was it? (*He remembers;
chuckling*) Oh yes, "Harvest Festivals". On the premise that "all is
safely gathered in." (*He chuckles again then hums his little tune*)

What? Did I touch her painkillers? I wouldn't know what her
painkillers looked like. Rosa Klebb keeps telling me off for mixing
up my own pills and potions, let alone anyone else's.

And what? Did I touch her? Did I touch Valerie? She is my wife, you
know. I am allowed to. Well, maybe a little peck on the cheek. No,
nothing more. When you get to my age you feel pretty good if you
can manage a peck on the cheek, let alone anything else.

Hands on her neck? I'm sorry, I don't know what you're talking about.
Anyway, what's all this to do with fixing my television aerial? Or are
you the toe-nail cutting people after all?

No, Valerie didn't say anything strange to me that evening. Didn't
say much. When you get to our age, you've exhausted most topics
of conversation.

Suns, eh? What suns? Suns of Saturn? Or is that rings? I can never
remember. Oh, my sons. Ah. Valerie's and my sons, yes, Miles and
Gavin. Fruit of our loins, eh? Our combined loins, that is. And we
did have a lot of fun combining our loins over the years. But that's
a long time ago.

You've met the boys, have you? Yes. There is said to be a family
likeness between us, though I can't see it myself. Anyway, we have
very different personalities. Be nice to say the boys haven't been
disappointments to me, but I can't. Gavin has no sense of morality.
Just doesn't understand the difference between right and wrong,
which I suppose is Valerie's and my fault. Blame the parents. (*He
hums his little tune*)

Bad with money, Gavin. Bit of a crook, I'm afraid. God, if I think of the number of times I've had to bail him out ... He'd do anything if he was going to get money out of it. I'd have washed my hands of him long ago, but Valerie insisted. Gavin could always get round Valerie. She loved him, I think. Fortunately, I suffer from no such sentimentality. Haven't seen Gavin for a while. Abroad, escaping creditors, I believe. Valerie kept in touch with him, constantly writing letters, told him everything.

What? Sorry, you'll have to speak up, young lady. My hearing's not what it was. Did she tell him about the new will? Oh yes, I'm sure she did.

My views on the will? There was a degree of logic in it, yes. I had already been putting things in Valerie's name. I knew my strength was failing, and my memory. It started with things at the office — papers I was sure I'd put down in a certain place, then turning up somewhere completely different. I began to lose confidence in my abilities. It couldn't have gone on like that. It made sense that I should retire from the practice, leave Miles to get on with it. And that Valerie should look after things at home. Though in the event, it wasn't Valerie, it was Miles there too. Miles controlling everything. He likes that. He likes control. He likes coercion.

No, it wouldn't be true to say he coerced me into signing the enduring power of attorney. I thought it was a good idea. To have the document there for when it was needed. I just hadn't imagined that Miles would put it into practice as soon as he did. Amazing the speed with which he got us both out of the big house, Valerie into the flat, me in here. Always a sharp practitioner, Miles.

What? Oh, I wouldn't say he would ever do anything criminal. Like most lawyers, he knows enough about the law to keep just the right side of it.

No, both boys have been a severe disappointment to me. Did I say that? There was a time when there was nearly a real scandal. Could have been a court case, all over the newspapers. Young woman claimed she'd been assaulted by one of my boys. Threatened to sue. I had to use all my skills as a mediator to settle that one. Cost me a lot of effort — not to mention money — to hush the thing up. And did I get any thanks for my efforts? You have to be joking. Never a great one for showing gratitude, Miles. But keeping the incident quiet made sense for a variety of reasons. Didn't want the company's name in the papers. And, you see, Miles was a partner at Trevelyan's.

Talked to Miles, have you? Oh, if you're going to see him again ... (*He reaches into his pocket and produces a pair of leather gloves*) Do give him these gloves. He must've left them by mistake when he came tell me about Valerie's death. Poor boy, must've been in shock. Why else would he put a perfectly decent pair of gloves in my wastepaper basket? And why had he got gloves with him in the middle of the summer? Luckily I managed to rescue the gloves before Rosa Klebb came to empty the bin. They do that morning and evening in this place, you know.

Oh, you want to take the gloves with you, do you? (*Rising out of his seat*) Yes, of course you can have them. (*He places the gloves on one of the chairs at the front*) I don't think you need bother putting them in a polythene bag like that. They're quite clean. Miles is a very hygienic sort of chap, you know, almost fastidious. Those gloves may have a bit of his sweat on them, and so on. But they're perfectly clean. Oh, well, you know your own business, I suppose.

Got to be off, have you? Turn off your little tape recorder, right. Recorded whatever it was you wanted to record, eh? Got to see Miles, right. Oh well, you make sure he gets his gloves back, won't you? Goodbye. It's been a pleasure to see you. (*Touching his head*) Oh, but you haven't done anything about my aerial, have you? Channel Five's still very fuzzy. Cheerio ... If you can't find your way out, Rosa Klebb'll help you.

He watches the detectives exit, humming his little tune, then he sits down again on his chair

Well, very satisfactory, I think. Miles learning rather late the lesson
that everyone should be aware of — that crime doesn't pay. Unless,
of course, you're a lawyer. (*He sniggers*) So all his clever plans, to
take over everything have come unstuck. I can't tell you how good
that knowledge makes me feel.

Being convicted of murdering Valerie is no less than he deserves. It
was he who started the process of disorienting me at Trevelyan's. I'm
sure he moved my papers around, so that I could never find anything.
I'm sure he tampered with my diary, so that I missed appointments.
It didn't take much to make me stop trusting myself. In all of us,
however in control we may appear, there is only a thin ricepaper of
confidence. Once that is breached, particularly as you get older, doubts
flood in. We all fear our minds going, we all panic when we cannot
remember. For all of us, the slippery slope is very near. The slippery
slope down which I have slipped.

I lost my nerve. I didn't make a fuss when Miles said I should come
in here. He'd shattered my confidence so completely that I thought
he was right. I thought my mind was totally gone. And then he started
putting pressure on Valerie. He was never going to get her the same
way. Even when the pain was eating away at her like acid, every one
of her marbles remained intact. Miles couldn't convince her that she
was losing her mind. So he dealt with her by an excess of solicitude.
Telling her the house she loved was too big, that she wouldn't be
safe in there. Telling her she needed sheltered housing in that pokey,
hideous little flat. Oh, he's a cool operator, Miles. And now he's got
his comeuppance. (*He chuckles*) Pity they no longer have the death
penalty for murder, but you can't have everything. Miles will get a
very long stretch, and, of course, a criminal is not allowed to profit
from his crimes, is he? That'll annoy him even more than being done
for murder. (*He chuckles, laughs and then is silent*) Particularly being
done for a murder he didn't commit. Oh, Miles was never capable of
working out something like this. He may have inherited a legal brain
from me, but it's not as good a brain as mine is.

Valerie and I worked it out together. The pain was becoming insufferable for her. There was no hope of her getting better, just waiting for the inevitable. At first, she resisted my suggestion for incriminating Miles. Sentimental woman, Valerie. But I won her round. We both agreed that we didn't mind having a son who was a crook, but we loathed having one who was a prig.

I'd been stockpiling her painkillers over the last six months. Just took one from her bedside table drawer each time I visited. Nobody noticed. And Miles was careless enough to leave his gloves here — round February, I suppose it was. He asked for them when he next came to visit me. I said I hadn't seen them.

It was Gavin's arrival which made us decide to do it last Wednesday. Now we'd got both of the vultures circling round. Hiding Miles' gloves from Rosa Klebb was easy — stuffed them in my cardigan. Same with the bottle of painkillers I'd crushed up and diluted. And I also took a pair of latex gloves from here. Lots of those around in a place like this, to handle a variety of noxious geriatric deposits. I put the latex ones on before I put on Miles's gloves, so that none of my DNA would be on the inside of them. Just his.

Valerie didn't mind it when I put my gloved hands on her neck and face. She said the different kind of pain was a welcome distraction from the other pain that burnt constantly through her body. She also said that what I was doing to her was almost erotic. (*He chuckles*) It did the business, anyway. Old flesh bruises very easily.

Valerie had a scarf ready to put round her throat, so that Miles wouldn't see anything untoward. And we said our goodbyes. We were giggly together, mischievous ... like we used to be before we had the children. Then I went and found Rosa Klebb to bring me back here.

I knew Valerie would fulfil her part of the bargain — wait 'til Miles had left and then swallow down her doctored drink, and find the peace she had been wishing for for so long.

He sighs, yawns, and looks at his watch

Nearly time for *Countdown*. I enjoy *Countdown*. I can always do more anagrams than the rest of the human flotsam and jetsom in this place. Not that I let anyone know that. No, no, I drool and mumble along with the rest of them. (*He rises and makes for the exit*) Which is what I'll do if Detective Inspector Maudsley and Detective Constable Parker reappear. I'll answer all their questions with a drool and a mumble, and possibly say that I think they've come to fix the television aerial on my head. And I'll do the same if they get me to stand up in court. After all, nobody's going to believe anything said by a gibbering old fool like me, are they?

He chuckles triumphantly, then exits, singing his tuneless little tune

The Lights fade to Black-out

THE END

FURNITURE AND PROPERTY LIST

Scene 1

On stage: Table
Three institutional chairs

Scene 2

No further props required

Scene 3

Personal: **Lionel**: leather gloves

LIGHTING PLOT

SCENE 1

To open: Interior lighting

| *Cue* 1 | **Gavin** storms off | (Page 7) |
| | *Fade to Black-out* | |

SCENE 2

To open: Interior lighting

| *Cue* 2 | **Miles** exits | (Page 11) |
| | *Fade to Black-out* | |

SCENE 3

To open: Interior lighting

| *Cue* 3 | **Lionel** exits, singing his tuneless little tune | (Page 19) |
| | *Fade to Black-out* | |

EFFECTS PLOT

No cues

Printed by The Kingfisher Press, London NW10 7AS

9 780573 142208